McGRAW-HILL
Language
Arts

Weekly
Grammar
Tests

with Writing Prompts

Grade 5

D1512601

Mc Graw Hill Macmillan
McGraw-Hill

New York   Farmington

Macmillan/McGraw-Hill

A Division of The McGraw-Hill Companies

Published by Macmillan/McGraw-Hill, a division of The McGraw-Hill Companies, Inc., Two Penn Plaza, New York, NY 10121

Printed in the United States of America

ISBN 0-02-244758-X/5

8 9 [042/042] 05 04

McGraw-Hill Language Arts
Weekly Grammar Tests
Grade 5

CONTENTS

McGraw-Hill Language Arts
WEEKLY GRAMMAR TESTS: STUDENT RECORD CHART

Name _____

Unit 1	Week 1		Week 2		Week 3		Week 4		Week 5	
	Item Numbers	Student Score	Item Numbers	Student Score	Item Numbers	Student Score	Item Numbers	Student Score	Item Numbers	Student Score
Grammar: Sentences										
Sentences and Fragments	1,2	/2							6,7	/2
Declarative and Interrogative	3,6	/2			1	/1			3,4	/2
Imperative and Exclamatory	4,5	/2			2	/1				
Combining Compound Sentences	7,8	/2					1,3	/2	1,2	/2
Complete Subjects and Predicates			1,2	/2	3	/1				
Simple Subjects			3,4	/2						
Simple Predicates			5,6	/2	4	/1				
Combining Compound Subjects			7	/1			2	/1		
Combining Compound Predicates			8	/1			4	/1	9	/1
Mechanics and Usage										
Sentence Punctuation	9,10,	/2							8	/1
Correcting Run-on Sentences			9,10	/2			5,6	/2	5,10	/2
Build Skills										
Study Skills: Note-Taking and Summarizing					7,8,9,10	/4				
Vocabulary: Time-Order Words					5,6	/2				
Writing										
Personal Narrative							7,8,9,10	/4		
TOTAL		/10		/10		/10		/10		/10
Writing Activity		/4		/4		/4		/4		/4

McGraw-Hill Language Arts
WEEKLY GRAMMAR TESTS: STUDENT RECORD CHART

Name _____

Unit 2	Week 1		Week 2		Week 3		Week 4		Week 5	
	Item Numbers	Student Score	Item Numbers	Student Score	Item Numbers	Student Score	Item Numbers	Student Score	Item Numbers	Student Score
Grammar: Nouns										
Nouns	1,2	/2							1, 2	/2
Singular and Plural Nouns	3,4	/2			1,2	/2			8	/1
More Plural Nouns (irregular forms)	5,6	/2			3,4	/2				
Common and Proper Nouns	7,8	/2							3,4	/2
Singular Possessive Nouns			1,2,3	/3			1	/1		
Plural Possessive Nouns			4,5,6	/3			2	/1	9	/1
Combining Sentences: Nouns			7,8	/2			3,4	/2		
Mechanics and Usage										
Capitalization	9,10	/2							5,6	/2
Letter Punctuation			9,10	/2			5,6	/2	7,10	/2
Build Skills										
Study Skills: Choose Reference Sources					7,8,9,10	/4				
Vocabulary: Compound Words					5,6	/2				
Writing										
Persuasive Writing							7,8,9,10	/4		
TOTAL		/10		/10		/10		/10		/10
Writing Activity		/4		/4		/4		/4		/4

McGraw-Hill Language Arts
WEEKLY GRAMMAR TESTS: STUDENT RECORD CHART

Name _____

Unit 3	Week 1		Week 2		Week 3		Week 4		Week 5	
	Item Numbers	Student Score	Item Numbers	Student Score	Item Numbers	Student Score	Item Numbers	Student Score	Item Numbers	Student Score
Grammar: Verbs										
Action Verbs	1,2	/2			1	/1				
Direct Objects	3,4	/2			2	/1				
Verb Tenses	5,6	/2			3	/1				
Subject-Verb Agreement	7,8	/2			4	/1				
Spelling Present- and Past-Tense Verbs	9	/1					1,2	/2	9	/1
Main Verbs and Helping Verbs			1,2	/2			5,6	/2		
Using Helping Verbs			3,4	/2					10	/1
Linking Verbs			5,6	/2					1,8	/2
Irregular Verbs			7,8	/2					2	/1
More Irregular Verbs			9	/1					3,4	/2
Mechanics and Usage										
Commas	10	/1					3,4	/2	7	/1
Contractions with *Not*									5,6	/2
Build Skills										
Study Skills: Encyclopedia			10	/1	7,8,9,10	/4				
Vocabulary: Prefixes and Suffixes					5,6	/2				
Writing										
Explanatory Writing							7,8,9,10	/4		
TOTAL		/10		/10		/10		/10		/10
Writing Activity		/4		/4		/4		/4		/4

McGraw-Hill Language Arts
WEEKLY GRAMMAR TESTS: STUDENT RECORD CHART

Name _____

Unit 4	Week 1		Week 2		Week 3		Week 4		Week 5	
	Item Numbers	Student Score	Item Numbers	Student Score	Item Numbers	Student Score	Item Numbers	Student Score	Item Numbers	Student Score
Grammar: Adjectives										
Adjectives	1,2,3	/3			1	/1				
Articles	4,5,6	/3			2	/1			7	/1
Demonstrative Adjectives	7,8	/2			3,4	/2			9	/1
Comparative and Superlative Adjectives			1,2	/2			3,4	/2	10	/1
Comparing with *More* and *Most*			3,4	/2			5,6	/2		
Comparing with *Good* and *Bad*			5,6	/2					1,2	/2
Combining Sentences: Adjectives			7,8	/2					3,4,8	/3
Mechanics and Usage										
Proper Adjectives	9,10	/2					1,2	/2		
Abbreviations			9,10	/2					5,6	/2
Build Skills										
Study Skills: Time Lines and Historical Maps					7,8,9,10	/4				
Vocabulary: Synonyms and Antonyms					5,6	/2				
Writing										
Expository Writing							7,8,9,10	/4		
TOTAL		/10		/10		/10		/10		/10
Writing Activity		/4		/4		/4		/4		/4

McGraw-Hill Language Arts
WEEKLY GRAMMAR TESTS: STUDENT RECORD CHART

Name _____

Unit 5	Week 1		Week 2		Week 3		Week 4		Week 5	
	Item Numbers	Student Score	Item Numbers	Student Score	Item Numbers	Student Score	Item Numbers	Student Score	Item Numbers	Student Score
Grammar: Pronouns										
Pronouns	1,2,3	/3			1,2	/2				
Subject Pronouns	4,5,6	/3			3,4	/2				
Object Pronouns	7,8	/2					1,2	/2	10	/1
Pronoun-Verb Agreement			1,2,3	/3			5,6	/2	8	/1
Combining Sentences: Subject and Object Pronouns			4,5,6	/3					1,2	/2
Possessive Pronouns			7,8	/2					3,4,7	/3
Mechanics and Usage										
Colons and Hyphens	9,10	/2					3,4	/2	9	/1
Contractions: Pronouns and Verbs			9,10	/2					5,6	/2
Build Skills										
Study Skills: Dictionary					7,8,9,10	/4				
Vocabulary: Word Choice					5,6	/2				
Writing										
Writing That Compares							7,8,9,10	/4		
TOTAL		/10		/10		/10		/10		/10
Writing Activity		/4		/4		/4		/4		/4

McGraw-Hill Language Arts
WEEKLY GRAMMAR TESTS: STUDENT RECORD CHART

Name _____

Unit 6	Week 1		Week 2		Week 3		Week 4		Week 5	
	Item Numbers	Student Score	Item Numbers	Student Score	Item Numbers	Student Score	Item Numbers	Student Score	Item Numbers	Student Score
Grammar: Adverbs, Prepositions and Interjections										
Adverbs	1,2	/2			1	/1				
Adverbs Before Adjectives and Adverbs	4,5	/2			2	/1				
Comparing with Adverbs	3,6	/2			3,4	/2			10	/1
Negatives							1,2	/2	8	/1
Prepositions			1,2	/2			3	/1		
Prepositional Phrases			3,4	/2			4,5	/2		
Object Pronouns in Prepositional Phrases			5,6	/2			6	/1		
Interjections									7	/1
Combining Sentences: Complex Sentences			7,8	/2					1,2	/2
Mechanics and Usage										
Punctuation in Dialogue	7,8,9,10	/4							3,9	/2
Commas with Introductory Prepositional Phrases and Interjections			9,10	/2					4,5,6	/3
Build Skills										
Study Skills: Card Catalog					7,8,9,10	/4				
Vocabulary: Figurative Language					5,6	/2				
Writing										
Story Writing							7,8,9,10	/4		
TOTAL		/10		/10		/10		/10		/10
Writing Activity		/4		/4		/4		/4		/4

Personal Narrative

Scoring Rubric

4. EXCELLENT

Ideas & Content
- creates a focused, extensively-detailed piece of writing; expresses fresh insights about the topic

Organization
- unfolds a carefully-organized story, in a sequence that moves the reader smoothly through the text

Voice
- conveys a reflective personal message that speaks directly to the reader; is deeply involved with the topic

Word Choice
- uses both original and everyday language in a natural way; uses sophisticated vocabulary that creates a striking picture and brings the story to life

Sentence Fluency
- creative, effective sentences flow in a smooth rhythm; dialogue, if used, sounds natural and strengthens the story

Conventions
- is skilled in most writing conventions; proper use of the rules of English enhances clarity and narrative style

3. GOOD

Ideas & Content
- crafts a clear, substantial piece of writing; details help convey key ideas and insights to the reader

Organization
- shows a well-planned narrative strategy; story is easy to follow; ideas are evenly tied together

Voice
- makes a strong effort to share an original personal message; connects with the purpose and audience; attempts to explore a range of feelings

Word Choice
- uses words that fit the story and create an accurate picture; experiments with some new words

Sentence Fluency
- crafts easy-to-follow sentences; may effectively use fragments and/or dialogue to enhance the story

Conventions
- spelling, capitalization, punctuation and usage are mostly correct; minor errors don't interfere with following the story; some editing may be needed

2. FAIR

Ideas & Content
- attempts to address the topic, but may not elaborate clearly or may lose control; details may be general, or unrelated to the topic

Organization
- may not have clear story structure, or may have trouble tying ideas together; reader may be confused by vague details

Voice
- tells a story, but in a predictable way; gets the message across, but does not seem involved with the topic or audience

Word Choice
- may not use words that convey strong feelings or images; words are overused, or may not fit the story purpose

Sentence Fluency
- may have trouble with complicated structures; sentences may be choppy, rambling, or awkward

Conventions
- makes frequent, noticeable mistakes which interfere with a smooth reading of the story; extensive editing is needed

1. UNSATISFACTORY

Ideas & Content
- does not tell a personal story; writer may go off in several directions, without a sense of purpose

Organization
- writing is hard to follow; story sequence is disorganized or incomplete; ideas and details are not tied together

Voice
- is not involved in sharing an experience with a reader; does not focus on anything of personal importance or interest; writing is flat and lifeless

Word Choice
- has a hard time finding the right words; may use words that do not fit the topic; some vocabulary detracts from the meaning of the text

Sentence Fluency
- sentences are incomplete, rambling, or confusing; may have trouble understanding how words and sentences fit together

Conventions
- makes errors in spelling, word choice, punctuation and usage; sentence structures may be confused; few connections made between ideas

0: This piece is either blank, or fails to respond to the writing task. The topic is not addressed, or the student simply paraphrases the prompt. The response may be illegible or incoherent.

Persuasive Writing

Scoring Rubric

4. EXCELLENT

Ideas & Content
- crafts an unusually compelling argument, with extensive supporting details; shares fresh insights

Organization
- keen, well-planned strategy moves the reader logically through the text; well-placed ideas and details heighten the impact

Voice
- conveys a powerful, authentic message, capable of convincing a listener; deep involvement with the topic enlivens the content and reaches out to affect the audience

Word Choice
- creative use of precise, sophisticated vocabulary helps to create a powerfully-convincing argument

Sentence Fluency
- varied, effective sentences flow naturally, uses both simple and complex sentences creatively; varied beginnings, lengths, and patterns

Conventions
- proper use of the rules of English enhances clarity, style, and cohesion of the argument; editing is largely unnecessary

3. GOOD

Ideas & Content
- crafts a well-thought-out argument; details show knowledge of the topic; may share some new insights

Organization
- audience can follow the writer's logic from beginning to end; details fit and build on each other

Voice
- clearly shows who is behind the words; personal style enhances the purpose of the speech; reaches out to convince the listener

Word Choice
- uses a variety of precise words to make the message clear; may experiment with new words, or use familiar words to share ideas in a fresh way

Sentence Fluency
- crafts careful sentences that make sense, and are easy to read and understand; sentence lengths vary, and fit together well

Conventions
- uses most conventions correctly; some editing may be needed; errors are few and don't make the paper hard to understand

2. FAIR

Ideas & Content
- attempts to craft a persuasive argument, but may not offer adequate facts and details

Organization
- has trouble consistently ordering information; states a main idea, but may not develop the persuasive form; poorly-placed details

Voice
- gives some hint of who is behind the words; writer may seem personally uninvolved

Word Choice
- gets the main idea across in a predictable way; experiments with few new words; may not choose strong enough words to influence a reader

Sentence Fluency
- sentences are understandable, but may be choppy, run-on, or awkward; writing is hard to follow

Conventions
- makes frequent noticeable mistakes which prevent a smooth reading of the text; extensive need for editing

1. UNSATISFACTORY

Ideas & Content
- does not successfully argue a position; it is hard to tell what the writer thinks or feels

Organization
- extreme lack of structure makes the text hard to follow; ideas, facts, and details are not connected

Voice
- writer does not understand or connect with the topic; is not involved in sharing ideas with a reader

Word Choice
- does not use words that express an opinion or attempt to convince a listener; words do not fit, or are overused

Sentence Fluency
- uses choppy, rambling, or confusing sentences; does not understand how words and sentences fit together; and is hard to read aloud

Conventions
- has severe errors in spelling, word choice, punctuation and usage; some parts are impossible to read or understand

0: This piece is either blank, or fails to respond to the writing task. The topic is not addressed, or the student simply paraphrases the prompt. The response may be illegible or incoherent.

Explanatory Writing

Scoring Rubric

4. EXCELLENT

Ideas & Content
- presents a focused, interesting how-to project, with an elaborate set of details

Organization
- easy-to-follow time sequence leads the reader logically through each stage; steps and details clarify the process

Voice
- exceptionally strong personal touch speaks to the reader, and enlivens the project content; cleverly connects the writing style to the purpose

Word Choice
- thoughtful, imaginative use of precise language creates a colorful picture of the how-to process

Sentence Fluency
- varied, well-crafted sentences flow with a natural rhythm; fragments, if used, add appeal to the explanation

Conventions
- proper use of the rules of English enhances clarity and personal style; editing largely unnecessary

3. GOOD

Ideas & Content
- presents a focused, interesting project, with details that clearly describe the main idea

Organization
- logical sequence helps a reader to follow the process from beginning to end; details are placed to make sense, and help to clarify each step

Voice
- genuine personal style reaches out to the reader, and shows who is behind the writing

Word Choice
- uses a variety of words that clarify the process; experiments with new words, or uses everyday words to present ideas in a fresh way

Sentence Fluency
- carefully-devised sentences are easy to read and follow; beginnings, lengths, and patterns vary and fit together

Conventions
- uses a variety of conventions correctly; some editing may be needed; errors are few

2. FAIR

Ideas & Content
- has some control of a how-to explanation, but may not offer clear or thorough details

Organization
- tries to structure a logical process, but may have trouble keeping ideas in order; reader may be confused by poorly-placed steps and details

Voice
- communicates ideas in an ordinary way; gives some hint of who is behind the words; may not show involvement with an audience, or with the topic project

Word Choice
- explores few new words; does not use accurate or colorful words to create a clear picture of the how-to process

Sentence Fluency
- may have trouble with more complex sentences; sentences are understandable, but may be choppy, rambling, or awkward?

Conventions
- makes frequent mistakes which may interfere with a smooth reading

1. UNSATISFACTORY

Ideas & Content
- does not explain a how-to process; writing may go off in several directions, without a sense of purpose

Organization
- does not present a clear structure; ideas are disconnected; no clear beginning or ending

Voice
- is not involved in the topic; lacks awareness of a reader

Word Choice
- does not use words that describe a process; some words may detract from the meaning of the text

Sentence Fluency
- constructs incomplete, rambling, or confusing sentences, which may interfere with following a process; does not understand how words and sentences fit together

Conventions
- makes repeated errors in spelling, word choice, punctuation and usage; sentence structures may be confused

0: This piece is either blank, or fails to respond to the writing task. The topic is not addressed, or the student simply paraphrases the prompt. The response may be illegible or incoherent.

Expository Writing

Scoring Rubric

4. EXCELLENT

Ideas & Content
- devises a focused, thoroughly-detailed report; makes fresh, accurate connections between key facts and observations

Organization
- careful structure moves the reader logically through the text; information and paragraphs are smoothly tied together

Voice
- shows deep involvement with the topic; distinct style enlivens the content; message is linked to the purpose and audience

Word Choice
- effective use of precise, colorful language makes the message clear and interesting; vocabulary is vivid and diverse, but natural

Sentence Fluency
- crafts fluid, simple and complex sentences; varied beginnings, lengths, and patterns add interest; effective use of sentences

Conventions
- correctly uses common and proper nouns; proper use of the rules of English enhances clarity, style, and cohesion of ideas; editing is largely unnecessary

3. GOOD

Ideas & Content
- presents a clear, carefully-researched report; details show knowledge of the topic; shares accurate information and observations

Organization
- logic is easy to follow; details fit, and reinforce facts; ideas, paragraphs, and sentences are connected

Voice
- is involved with the topic; devises a style that relates to the topic and audience

Word Choice
- uses a variety of words to create an accurate picture for the reader; experiments with challenging words, or uses everyday words in a fresh way

Sentence Fluency
- crafts simple and complex sentences that are easy to read aloud; lengths and patterns vary, and fit together well

Conventions
- uses a variety of conventions correctly; some editing may be needed; errors are few and don't make the paper hard to understand

2. FAIR

Ideas & Content
- details and ideas are vague, undeveloped, or do not fit; makes predictable observations about the topic

Organization
- tries to shape a report, but may have trouble ordering facts and comments; reader may be confused by vague or disconnected details

Voice
- may not connect a distinct personal message or style to the facts; is not very involved with the topic, or an audience

Word Choice
- gets the message across, in an average way; experiments with few new words; some words may not fit the topic

Sentence Fluency
- most sentences are understandable, but may be choppy, monotonous, or run-on; writer may have trouble with more complex sentences

Conventions
- makes noticeable mistakes that prevent a smooth reading of the text; extensive need for editing and revision

1. UNSATISFACTORY

Ideas & Content
- does not successfully report on the topic; writer may not grasp the purpose, or may offer very limited facts and ideas

Organization
- logic is hard to follow; ideas and details are disconnected, or out of order; no sense of a clear beginning or ending

Voice
- is not involved in the topic; does not try to convey a personal style or address ideas to an audience

Word Choice
- chooses words that don't fit, or which confuse reader; no new words are attempted; familiar words are overused

Sentence Fluency
- constructs incomplete or confusing sentences; does not grasp how words and sentences fit together; writing is hard to read aloud

Conventions
- makes repeated errors in word choice, punctuation and usage; spelling errors make it hard to guess what words are meant

0: This piece is either blank, or fails to respond to the writing task. The topic is not addressed, or the student simply paraphrases the prompt. The response may be illegible or incoherent.

Writing That Compares

Scoring Rubric

4. EXCELLENT

Ideas & Content
- skillfully compares two things; carefully-selected details clarify each comparison point

Organization
- careful strategy moves the reader smoothly through each point; well-placed observations and details strengthen the logic

Voice
- deep involvement with the topic enlivens the content; writer reaches out to share ideas with an audience

Word Choice
- makes imaginative use of strong, advanced vocabulary to describe explicit differences and similarities

Sentence Fluency
- varied sentences flow naturally; uses both simple and complex sentences; varied beginnings, lengths, and patterns add appeal

Conventions
- proper use of the rules of English enhances clarity and cohesion of the comparisons; editing is largely unnecessary

3. GOOD

Ideas & Content
- crafts a solid, well-thought-out comparison; details bring the main idea into focus; may share some new insights about their experiences

Organization
- presents a capable, solid strategy; reader can follow the logic from beginning to end; details fit and build on each other

Voice
- shows who is behind the words; personal style matches the purpose; reaches out to the reader

Word Choice
- uses a range of precise words to present facts and observations; explores some challenging words, or uses everyday words to state ideas in a fresh way

Sentence Fluency
- crafts careful sentences that make sense, and are easy to read and understand; sentence lengths and patterns vary, and fit together well

Conventions
- uses most conventions correctly; some editing may be needed; errors are few

2. FAIR

Ideas & Content
- has some control of the comparison task, but may offer limited or unclear facts and details; makes obvious connections about the topic

Organization
- tries to build a structure, but has trouble sequencing ideas; may not present distinct comparison categories; poorly-placed facts and details

Voice
- communicates a main idea, with some hint of who is behind the words; writer may seem personally uninvolved with the topic and an audience

Word Choice
- gets the argument across, but experiments with few new words

Sentence Fluency
- sentences are understandable, but may be choppy, rambling, or awkward; writing is difficult to follow or read aloud

Conventions
- frequent noticeable mistakes prevent an even reading of the text; extensive need for editing and revision

1. UNSATISFACTORY

Ideas & Content
- does not successfully compare two things; it is hard to tell what the writer intended to say

Organization
- extreme lack of structure makes the text hard to follow; ideas, facts, and details are disconnected, out of order

Voice
- does not connect with the topic; is not involved in sharing ideas with a reader

Word Choice
- does not use words that show differences or similarities; some words may detract from the purpose to compare; words do not fit, or are overused

Sentence Fluency
- uses choppy, rambling, or confusing sentences; does not understand how words and sentences fit together; writing doesn't follow natural sentence patterns, and is hard to read aloud

Conventions
- has repeated errors in spelling, word choice, punctuation and usage; some parts are impossible to read

0: This piece is either blank, or fails to respond to the writing task. The topic is not addressed, or the student simply paraphrases the prompt. The response may be illegible or incoherent.

4. EXCELLENT

Ideas & Content
- creates an entertaining, richly-detailed story; characters, setting, and events are skillfully developed

Organization
- unfolds a consistent, carefully-planned narrative; sequence moves the reader smoothly through events

Voice
- shows originality, liveliness, and a strong personal message that speaks directly to the reader

Word Choice
- imaginative use of figurative and everyday words brings the story to life; sophisticated vocabulary creates a striking picture of individual characters

Sentence Fluency
- crafts creative, effective sentences that flow in a smooth rhythm; dialogue, if used, sounds natural and animates the story

Conventions
- shows strong skills in a wide range of writing conventions; proper use of the rules of English enhances clarity and narrative style

3. GOOD

Ideas & Content
- presents a focused, interesting story with characters, setting, and events

Organization
- has a carefully-planned narrative strategy; story is easy to follow, through beginning, middle, and end; ideas are evenly connected

Voice
- makes a strong effort to share an authentic personal message that reaches out to an audience

Word Choice
- has overall clarity of expression; effective control of both new and everyday words

Sentence Fluency
- crafts careful, easy-to-follow sentences; may effectively use fragments and/or dialogue to strengthen and enhance the story

Conventions
- makes some errors in spelling, capitalization, punctuation or usage, but these do not interfere with understanding the story; some editing may be needed

2. FAIR

Ideas & Content
- attempts to write a story; may not elaborate adequately; may lose control of the narrative after a good beginning

Organization
- may not craft a clear story structure, or interferes with understanding the text; may have trouble tying ideas and events together; story line may be vague or incomplete

Voice
- may get the basic story across, without a sense of involvement of reaching out to an audience; writing is flat and lifeless

Word Choice
- does not explore words that express clear ideas or feelings; may not choose words that create memorable pictures for the reader

Sentence Fluency
- may have trouble with complex sentences; sentences are understandable, but may be choppy, rambling, or awkward

Conventions
- makes enough noticeable mistakes which may interfere with a smooth reading of the story

1. UNSATISFACTORY

Ideas & Content
- may not understand how to tell a story; narrative may go off in several directions, without a sense of purpose

Organization
- shows extreme lack of organization that interferes with understanding the text; sequence of events may be disorganized or incomplete

Voice
- does not attempt to make sense, share ideas, or connect with a reader

Word Choice
- does not choose words that convey clear feelings or images; some word choices may detract from the meaning of the story

Sentence Fluency
- constructs incomplete, rambling, or confusing sentences; may have trouble understanding how words, ideas, and sentences fit together

Conventions
- makes repeated errors in spelling, word choice, punctuation and usage; errors prevent an even reading of the text

0: This piece is either blank, or fails to respond to the writing task. The topic is not addressed, or the student simply paraphrases the prompt. The response may be illegible or incoherent.

Sentences

♦ Fill in the bubble next to the answer that corrects the sentence fragment.

Complete Sentences

1. Hunt mice and rats.

   ⓐ Expertly hunt mice and rats.   ⓑ Hunt mice and rats in barns.

   ⓒ Farm cats hunt mice and rats.   ⓓ Hunt mice and rats often.

2. Wild cats.

   ⓐ Wild cats and lions.   ⓑ Was afraid of wild cats.

   ⓒ Photographed wild cats.   **ⓓ** Wild cats move silently.

♦ Fill in the bubble next to the words that name the kind of sentence.

Declarative Sentences

3. Cats are mysterious and graceful animals.

   ⓐ declarative sentence   ⓑ interrogative sentence

   ⓒ imperative sentence   ⓓ exclamatory sentence

Imperative Sentences

4. Watch the cat pounce upon its prey.

   ⓐ declarative sentence   ⓑ interrogative sentence

   ⓒ imperative sentence   ⓓ exclamatory sentence

Exclamatory Sentences

5. How fast she can climb the trunk!

   ⓐ declarative sentence   ⓑ interrogative sentence

   ⓒ imperative sentence   **ⓓ** exclamatory sentence

Interrogative Sentences

6. Do many cats get trapped in trees?

   ⓐ declarative sentence   **ⓑ** interrogative sentence

   ⓒ imperative sentence   ⓓ exclamatory sentence

GO ON ▶

♦ Fill in the bubble next to the best way to combine the sentences.

Combining Sentences: Compound Sentences

7. I like to play basketball. My brother does not.

ⓐ I like to play basketball and my brother does not.

ⓑ I like to play basketball, my brother does not.

ⓒ I like to play basketball, but my brother does not.

ⓓ I like to play basketball but my brother does not.

8. I practice basketball every day. My skills are improving.

ⓐ I practice basketball every day, my skills are improving.

ⓑ I practice basketball every day but my skills are improving.

ⓒ I practice basketball every day or my skills are improving.

ⓓ I practice basketball every day, and my skills are improving.

♦ Fill in the bubble next to the correct sentence.

Mechanics and Usage: Sentence Punctuation

9. ⓐ Robert took a shot but the ball bounced off the rim?

ⓑ Robert took a shot but the ball bounced off the rim.

ⓒ Robert took a shot but, the ball bounced off the rim.

ⓓ Robert took a shot, but the ball bounced off the rim.

10. ⓐ Jump high! And catch the ball.

ⓑ Jump high, and catch the ball.

ⓒ Jump high, and catch the ball?

ⓓ Jump high and, catch the ball.

♦ Choose a sport you like to play or watch. Write a paragraph telling a friend to try the sport. Include different types of sentences in your paragraph.

Sentences

♦ Fill in the bubble next to the part of the sentence named in bold.

Complete Subjects and Complete Predicates

1. Our shining sun is a huge ball of gas called a star. **complete subject**

   ⓐ sun   ⬤ⓑ Our shining sun

   ⓒ shining sun   ⓓ Our shining sun is a huge ball

2. This star gives us light and heat. **complete predicate**

   ⓐ star gives us light and heat   ⓑ gives

   ⬤ⓒ gives us light and heat   ⓓ light and heat

Simple Subjects

3. The stars in our galaxy make up a small part of the universe. **simple subject**

   ⬤ⓐ stars   ⓑ The stars

   ⓒ galaxy   ⓓ our galaxy

4. Our science class looked at stars through a telescope. **simple subject**

   ⓐ Our science class   ⓑ science

   ⓒ looked   ⬤ⓓ class

Simple Predicates

5. Most stars appear as tiny points of light. **simple predicate**

   ⓐ stars   ⬤ⓑ appear

   ⓒ light   ⓓ points

6. Some stars are much larger than our sun. **simple predicate**

   ⬤ⓐ are   ⓑ sun

   ⓒ larger   ⓓ stars

GO ON ▶

Name_____ Date_____

♦ Fill in the bubble next to the best way to combine the sentences.

Combining Sentences: Compound Subjects

7. Jazz is my favorite kind of music. Rock is my favorite kind of music.

    ⓐ Jazz and rock are my favorite kinds of music.

    ⓑ Jazz, rock are my favorite kinds of music.

    ⓒ Jazz and rock, is my favorite kind of music.

    ⓓ Jazz, and rock is my favorite kind of music.

Combining Sentences: Compound Predicates

8. Jenni reads after school. Jenni studies after school.

    ⓐ Jenni reads after school, studies after school.

    ⓑ Jenni reads after school, or Jenni studies.

    ⓒ Jenni reads, and studies after school.

    ⓓ Jenni reads and studies after school.

♦ Fill in the bubble next to the best way to correct the run-on sentence.

Mechanics and Usage: Correct Run-on Sentences

9. Mrs. Wilson likes opera her cousin took her to see *Tosca*.

    ⓐ Mrs. Wilson likes opera and her cousin took her to see *Tosca*.

    ⓑ Mrs. Wilson likes opera and her cousin. Took her to see *Tosca*.

    ⓒ Mrs. Wilson likes opera. Her cousin took her to see *Tosca*.

    ⓓ Mrs. Wilson likes opera, her cousin took her to see *Tosca*.

10. John can play the guitar Sara can play the drums.

    ⓐ John can play the guitar but Sara can play the drums.

    ⓑ John can play the guitar, but Sara can play the drums.

    ⓒ John can play the guitar, Sara can play the drums.

    ⓓ John can play the guitar or, Sara can play the drums.

♦ Write a description of a concert you would like to attend. Underline the simple subjects and circle the simple predicates.

Sentences/Build Skills

♦ Fill in the bubble next to the words that name the kind of sentence.

Declarative Sentences

1. Juliana looked through her family picture album.

   ⓐ declarative sentence   ⓑ interrogative sentence

   ⓒ imperative sentence   ⓓ exclamatory sentence

Exclamatory Sentences

2. What a surprise she had!

   ⓐ declarative sentence   ⓑ interrogative sentence

   ⓒ imperative sentence   ⓓ exclamatory sentence

♦ Fill in the bubble next to the words that name the underlined part of the sentence.

Complete Subjects and Complete Predicates

3. <u>Her great-grandmother</u> wore a bracelet in one of the photographs.

   ⓐ simple subject   ⓑ complete subject

   ⓒ simple predicate   ⓓ complete predicate

Simple Predicates

4. Juliana <u>owns</u> a bracelet just like it.

   ⓐ simple subject   ⓑ complete subject

   ⓒ simple predicate   ⓓ complete predicate

♦ Fill in the bubble next to the time-order word or words from the sentence.

Time-Order Words

5. After noticing the bracelet, Juliana showed the photograph to her mother.

   ⓐ After   ⓑ noticing

   ⓒ showed   ⓓ to her mother

GO ON ➤

6. She will add her own picture to the family album tomorrow.

    ⓐ She will   ⓑ add

    ⓒ her own   ⓓ tomorrow

◆ Fill in the bubble next to the best answer.

Using Note-Taking and Summarizing Skills

7. What is the most important reason to take notes?

    ⓐ to help you find more information

    ⓑ to practice using primary sources

    ⓒ to help you remember what you read

    ⓓ to practice writing summaries

8. Which of these should NOT be included in a summary?

    ⓐ main ideas   ⓑ supporting details

    ⓒ important facts   ⓓ minor details

Composition: Main Ideas and Details

9. The main idea of a paragraph is usually stated in the _____.

    ⓐ topic sentence   ⓑ detail sentence

    ⓒ final sentence   ⓓ time-order sentence

10. A supporting detail _____.

    ⓐ replaces the main idea

    ⓑ adds to the main idea

    ⓒ must tell about a personal experience

    ⓓ always tells the purpose for writing

◆ Think of a time when you learned how to do an activity, such as riding a bicycle or swimming. Write a paragraph telling how you learned to do this activity. Use time-order words to show the sequence of events. Underline the topic sentence of the paragraph, and circle the time-order words.

▢ 10

Sentences/Personal Narrative

♦ Fill in the bubble next to the best way to combine the sentences.

Combining Sentences: Compound Sentences

1. Jon likes dates. Ali likes figs.

   ⓐ Jon likes dates, Ali likes figs.   ⓑ Jon likes dates, and Ali likes figs.

   ⓒ Jon likes dates and Ali likes figs.   ⓓ Jon or Ali likes apples, and figs.

Combining Sentences: Compound Subjects

2. Pears are sweet. Peaches are sweet.

   ⓐ Pears are sweet, and peaches.   ⓑ Pears are sweet and peaches are.

   ⓒ Pears and peaches are sweet.   ⓓ Pears, or peaches are sweet.

Combining Sentences: Compound Sentences

3. I love peach pie. Ben does not.

   ⓐ I love peach pie and Ben does not.   ⓑ I love peach pie but, not Ben.

   ⓒ I love peach pie, Ben does not.   ⓓ I love peach pie, but Ben does not.

Combining Sentences: Compound Predicates

4. We peeled the peaches for the pie. We sliced the peaches for the pie.

   ⓐ We peeled and sliced the peaches for the pie.

   ⓑ We peeled the peaches for the pie and we sliced the peaches for the pie.

   ⓒ We peeled the peaches for the pie, but we sliced the peaches for the pie.

   ⓓ We peeled the peaches for the pie and we sliced.

♦ Fill in the bubble next to the best way to correct the sentence.

Mechanics and Usage: Corrects Run-On Sentences

5. john mixed the pie dough then my mother rolled it

   ⓐ John mixed the pie dough then my mother rolled it.

   ⓑ John mixed the pie dough, and then my mother rolled it.

   ⓒ John mixed the pie dough and then my mother rolled it?

   ⓓ John mixed the pie dough, Then my mother rolled it.

GO ON ➤

6. i ran inside to taste the pie it was still too hot

ⓐ I ran inside to taste the pie, It was still too hot!

ⓑ I ran inside to taste the pie and it was still too hot.

ⓒ I ran inside to taste the pie, but it was still too hot.

ⓓ I ran inside to taste the pie but it was still too hot!

♦ Fill in the bubble next to the best answer.

Writing: Personal Narrative

7. Which of these is the best topic for a personal narrative?

ⓐ the main parts of a computer　　ⓑ my first day at a new school

ⓒ the life of a historical figure　　ⓓ the causes of World War II

8. The first-person point of view shows that the experience happened
_____.

ⓐ recently　　　　　　　　ⓑ long ago

ⓒ to the author　　　　　　ⓓ to someone else

9. Which of the following is a time-order word?

ⓐ there　　　　　　　　　ⓑ finally

ⓒ wait　　　　　　　　　　ⓓ behind

10. Time-order words are important in personal narratives because they
show _____.

ⓐ which events are most important　　ⓑ where the events happened

ⓒ the sequence of the events　　　　　ⓓ the cause of the events

♦ Think about a time when you met someone new. Make a main idea map to organize your ideas and write a paragraph about the meeting and how you felt about it. Use the first-person point of view and time-order words.

10

Sentences/Personal Narrative

♦ Fill in the bubble next to the best way to combine the sentences.

Combining Sentences: Compound Sentences

1. Ponds are small and shallow. They are home to many plants.

   ⓐ Ponds are small and shallow, but they are home to many plants.

   ⓑ Ponds are small, and shallow, they are home to many plants.

   ⓒ Ponds are small and shallow, and are home to many plants.

   ⓓ Ponds are small and shallow and they are home to many plants.

2. Some plants float. Others are rooted to the bottom.

   ⓐ Some plants float but, others are rooted to the bottom.

   ⓑ Some plants float, Others are rooted to the bottom.

   ⓒ Some plants float, but others are rooted to the bottom.

   ⓓ Some plants float, others are rooted to the bottom.

♦ Fill in the bubble next to the punctuation mark that should end each sentence.

Declarative Sentences/Mechanics and Usage: Sentence Punctuation

3. The water level of a pond changes frequently due to rainfall

   ⓐ comma   ⓑ period

   ⓒ question mark   ⓓ exclamation point

Interrogative Sentences/Mechanics and Usage: Sentence Punctuation

4. How do underwater plants get oxygen

   ⓐ comma   ⓑ period

   ⓒ question mark   ⓓ exclamation point

♦ Fill in the bubble next to the best way to correct the sentences.

Complete Sentences

5. Eats flies and other insects.

   ⓐ Eats flies, and other insects.   ⓑ Eats flies, other insects.

   ⓒ Quickly eats flies and other insects.   ⓓ A frog eats flies and other insects.

GO ON ➤

Mechanics and Usage: Corrects Run-On Sentences

6. Dragonflies often live near ponds they lay their eggs in the water.

ⓐ Dragonflies often live near ponds and they lay their eggs in the water.

ⓑ Dragonflies often live near ponds, they lay their eggs in the water.

🅒 Dragonflies often live near ponds. They lay their eggs in the water.

ⓓ Dragonflies often live near ponds but, they lay their eggs in the water.

◆ Fill in the bubble next to the best way to correct each underlined section.

<u>Went to the beach.</u> We watched a sand sculpture competition. <u>What an</u>
                    7   **8**
<u>amazing sight?</u> <u>We entered the contest and built an igloo out of sand.</u>
                                                        9
<u>It took hours to complete we had a great time.</u>
            10

Complete Sentences

7. ⓐ Usually went to the beach.   🅑 My family went to the beach.

ⓒ Went to the beach finally.   ⓓ Correct as is

Mechanics and Usage: Sentence Punctuation

8. ⓐ What an amazing sight.   🅑 What an amazing sight!

ⓒ What an amazing sight,   ⓓ Correct as is

Combining Sentences: Compound Predicates

9. ⓐ We entered the contest, and built an igloo out of sand.

ⓑ We entered the contest. Built an igloo out of sand.

ⓒ We entered the contest, built an igloo out of sand.

🅓 Correct as is

Mechanics and Usage: Corrects Run-On Sentences

10. ⓐ It took hours to complete, we had a great time.

🅑 It took hours to complete, but we had a great time.

ⓒ It took hours to complete and, we had a great time.

ⓓ Correct as is

◆ Write a personal narrative about a contest in which you competed.

Nouns

♦ Fill in the bubble next to a noun from each sentence.

Nouns

1. Birds called nightingales are famous for their beautiful songs.

    ⓐ famous 　　　 ⓑ called

    ⓒ songs 　　　 ⓓ beautiful

Nouns

2. A tiny hummingbird beats its wings dozens of times each second.

    ⓐ beats 　　　 ⓑ second

    ⓒ each 　　　 ⓓ tiny

♦ Fill in the bubble next to the correct form of the noun.

Singular and Plural Nouns

3. The world's largest birds are _____.

    ⓐ ostrich 　　　 ⓑ ostrichs

    ⓒ ostriches 　　　 ⓓ ostrichies

Singular and Plural Nouns

4. Falcons, _____, and hawks are birds of prey.

    ⓐ eagle 　　　 ⓑ eagles

    ⓒ eagls 　　　 ⓓ eagleys

♦ Fill in the bubble next to the plural form of the word in bold.

More (Irregular) Plural Nouns

5. The cardinals looked great in the set of **photo.**

    ⓐ photo 　　　 ⓑ photeos

    ⓒ photios 　　　 ⓓ photos

GO ON ➤

More (Irregular) Plural Nouns

6. The flock of ducks ate two entire **loaf** of bread.

ⓐ loafs   ⓑ loafes

ⓒ loaves   ⓓ leef

◆ Fill in the bubble next to the kind of noun shown in bold.

Common and Proper Nouns

7. After she got a new job, my aunt moved to California. **proper noun**

ⓐ she   ⓑ aunt

ⓒ After   ⓓ California

Common and Proper Nouns

8. She visited parks at the Grand Canyon and the Painted Desert on her drive through Arizona. **common noun**

ⓐ parks   ⓑ Grand Canyon

ⓒ Painted Desert   ⓓ visited

◆ Fill in the bubble next to the word that should be capitalized.

Capitalization

9. In july, our family will take a trip to my aunt's new home.

ⓐ July   ⓑ Family

ⓒ Trip   ⓓ Home

Capitalization

10. She will probably take us to watch fireworks at the park on Independence day.

ⓐ Us   ⓑ Fireworks

ⓒ Park   ⓓ Day

◆ Make a travel brochure about a place you would like to visit. Underline each common noun in your paragraph, and circle each proper noun.

Nouns

♦ Fill in the bubble next to the possessive form of the noun in bold.

Singular Possessive Nouns

1. **John** dog is a border collie named Rowdy.

   ⓐ Johns'   ⓑ John's

   ⓒ Johns's   ⓓ Johns

Singular Possessive Nouns

2. John was proud of his **collie** ability to do tricks.

   ⓐ collies   ⓑ collies'

   ⓒ collie's   ⓓ collies's

Singular Possessive Nouns

3. He entered Rowdy in the **city** dog show.

   ⓐ city's   ⓑ citie's

   ⓒ cities   ⓓ citys'

Plural Possessive Nouns

4. Many of the other **dogs** skills were excellent.

   ⓐ doges's   ⓑ dogses'

   ⓒ dogs's   ⓓ dogs'

Plural Possessive Nouns

5. The three **judges** decision was final, and Rowdy won first prize.

   ⓐ judge's   ⓑ judges'

   ⓒ judgess's   ⓓ judgeses'

Plural Possessive Nouns

6. The **children** loud cheering made John and Rowdy proud.

   ⓐ childrens's   ⓑ children's

   ⓒ children'   ⓓ childrens'

GO ON ➤

Name_____ Date_____

♦ Fill in the bubble next to the best way to combine the sentences by joining nouns.

Nouns

7. You can do great tricks on a skateboard. You can do great stunts on a skateboard.

   ⓐ You can do great tricks and stunts on a skateboard.

   ⓑ You can do great tricks on a skateboard and great stunts on a skateboard.

   ⓒ You can do great tricks and you can do great stunts on a skateboard.

   ⓓ You can do great tricks on a skateboard and you can do great stunts.

Nouns

8. Skateboards are made of wood. Skateboards are made of fiberglass.

   ⓐ Skateboards are made of wood or made of fiberglass.

   ⓑ Skateboards are made of wood or skateboards are made of fiberglass.

   ⓒ Skateboards are made of wood or skateboards of fiberglass.

   ⓓ Skateboards are made of wood or fiberglass.

♦ Fill in the bubble next to the best way to write each phrase from a letter.

Letter Punctuation

9. ⓐ Sincerely Yours   ⓑ Sincerely yours:

   ⓒ Sincerely yours,   ⓓ sincerely yours

Letter Punctuation

10. ⓐ March,12, 2001   ⓑ March 12. 2001.

    ⓒ March, 12, 2001.   ⓓ March 12, 2001

♦ Write a letter to a friend. Ask your friend to help you plan a party for a classmate. Be sure to use the correct punctuation for a friendly letter. Underline the singular possessive nouns you use once, and underline the plural possessive nouns twice.

Nouns/Build Skills

♦ Fill in the bubble next to the kind of noun named in bold.

Singular and Plural Nouns

1. My hat has colorful stripes and dots. **singular noun**

   ⓐ hat   ⓑ colorful

   ⓒ stripes   ⓓ dots

Singular and Plural Nouns

2. The beautiful colors of the blanket brighten up the room. **plural noun**

   ⓐ blanket   ⓑ brighten

   ⓒ colors   ⓓ room

♦ Fill in the bubble next to the plural form of the noun in bold.

More (Irregular) Plural Nouns

3. My uncles are **fisherman,** and they brought me a squid they caught.

   ⓐ fishermen   ⓑ fishermans

   ⓒ fishersmen   ⓓ fisherman's

More (Irregular) Plural Nouns

4. My uncle's book **shelf** are filled with books about the sea.

   ⓐ shelfs   ⓑ shelfes

   ⓒ shelves   ⓓ shelvs

♦ Fill in the bubble next to the compound word from the sentence.

Compound Words

5. I love the beautiful fish in my aquarium, but the angelfish is my favorite.

   ⓐ beautiful fish   ⓑ aquarium

   ⓒ angelfish   ⓓ favorite

GO ON ▶

Compound Words

6. An aquarium requires an air pump and a bright light.

   (a) air pump   (b) aquarium

   (c) requires   (d) bright light

♦ Fill in the bubble next to the best source to answer the question.

Choose Reference Sources

7. Where is the Kalahari Desert?

   (a) dictionary   (b) thesaurus

   (c) atlas   (d) almanac

Choose Reference Sources

8. What is another word for *amazing*?

   (a) *Reader's Guide to Periodical Literature*   (b) atlas

   (c) encyclopedia   (d) thesaurus

Choose Reference Sources

9. Which football team won the Super Bowl in 1999?

   (a) dictionary   (b) almanac

   (c) *Reader's Guide to Periodical Literature*   (d) encyclopedia

Choose Reference Sources

10. Who was the author of a recent magazine article about robots?

   (a) *Reader's Guide to Periodical Literature*   (b) thesaurus

   (c) almanac   (d) encyclopedia

♦ Write a short speech in which you try to persuade a family member to go to a movie or play. Begin with a strong lead and close with a good ending. Circle any compound words you use.

Nouns/Persuasive Writing

♦ Fill in the bubble next to the possessive form of the noun in bold.

Singular Possessive Nouns

1. We love to walk along the **park** trails.

   ⓐ park's   ⓑ parks's

   ⓒ parks'   ⓓ parkes'

   Plural Possessive Nouns

2. Baseball **players** uniforms may be plain or striped.

   ⓐ players's   ⓑ players'es

   ⓒ playerses'   ⓓ players'

♦ Fill in the bubble next to the best way to combine the sentences by joining nouns.

Nouns

3. Pines are green. Firs are green.

   ⓐ Pines are green, and firs are green.   ⓑ Pines are green and firs are green.

   ⓒ Pines and firs are green.   ⓓ Pines are green and firs.

   Nouns

4. Ants march up tree trunks. Ants march up tree branches.

   ⓐ Ants march up tree trunks, and march up tree branches.

   ⓑ Ants march up tree trunks, and ants march up tree branches.

   ⓒ Ants and tree branches march up tree trunks.

   ⓓ Ants march up tree trunks and branches.

♦ Fill in the bubble next to the best answer.

Letter Punctuation

5. Which punctuation mark should follow the greeting of a business letter?

   ⓐ comma   ⓑ semicolon

   ⓒ colon   ⓓ period

GO ON ➡

Letter Punctuation

6. In the heading of a letter, what is used between the name of a city and state?

    ⓐ comma   ⓑ semicolon

    ⓒ colon   ⓓ dash

♦ Fill in the bubble next to the best answer.

Writing

7. What is the main purpose of persuasive writing?

    ⓐ to entertain the audience   ⓑ to convince others

    ⓒ to explain the causes of an event   ⓓ to describe personal experiences

Writing

8. Which would be the best topic for persuasive writing?

    ⓐ How to Build a Dog House   ⓑ Skaters Should Wear Helmets

    ⓒ What I Did During Spring Break   ⓓ Are Venus and Earth Similar?

Writing

9. Which sentence uses opinion words?

    ⓐ Light from cities can block light from stars.

    ⓑ People can see more stars in the country than in the city.

    ⓒ Obviously, the best solution is to use fewer lights at night.

    ⓓ Some people could use timers to turn off some lights.

Writing

10. In persuasive writing, where does the strongest argument usually come?

    ⓐ first   ⓑ last

    ⓒ in the middle   ⓓ in the lead

♦ Think about how you could persuade your school to observe a recycling day. Make a reason-and-explanation chart to organize your ideas. Then use your chart to help you write a persuasive paragraph.

Nouns/Persuasive Writing

♦ Fill in the bubble next to the type of word shown in bold.

Nouns

1. Amy heard her mother open the front door. **noun**

   ⓐ heard   ⓑ open

   ⓒ Amy   ⓓ front

Nouns

2. Amy's mother held a strange package under her arm. **noun**

   ⓐ strange   ⓑ package

   ⓒ held   ⓓ under

Common and Proper Nouns

3. Amy saw an oil painting from artist Patricia Spilman. **proper noun**

   ⓐ saw   ⓑ oil painting

   ⓒ artist   ⓓ Patricia Spilman

Common and Proper Nouns

4. The painting showed the dawn sky behind the Eiffel Tower. **common noun**

   ⓐ sky   ⓑ Eiffel Tower

   ⓒ showed   ⓓ behind

♦ Fill in the bubble next to the sentence with correct capitalization.

Capitalization

5. ⓐ The title was *Summer Of light.*   ⓑ The title was *Summer of Light.*

   ⓒ The title was *Summer of light.*   ⓓ The title was *summer Of Light.*

Capitalization

6. ⓐ She will show it to Mr. Garcia on Thursday.

   ⓑ She will show it to Mr. garcia on thursday.

   ⓒ She will show it to mr. Garcia on Thursday.

   ⓓ She will show it to mr. Garcia on thursday.

GO ON ➤

Name_____ Date_____

♦ Fill in the bubble next to the best way to correct each underlined section.

<u>Dear Principal Walters</u>
7

Have you noticed that there are no trash cans on our <u>school buses</u>
8

<u>Students' trash</u> often ends up on the floor. Each bus should have a small
9

trash can at the front, so we can help keep the bus cleaner. Please consider

our suggestion.

<u>sincerely</u>
10

Ms. Ahn's fifth-grade class

Letter Punctuation

7. ⓐ Dear Principal Walters.   ⓑ Dear Principal Walters:

   ⓒ dear Principal Walters,   ⓓ Correct as is

Punctuation

8. ⓐ school buses.   ⓑ school buses?

   ⓒ school buses,   ⓓ Correct as is

Plural Possessive Nouns

9. ⓐ Students's trash   ⓑ Student's trash

   ⓒ Students trash   ⓓ Correct as is

Letter Punctuation

10. ⓐ Sincerely,   ⓑ sincerely,

    ⓒ Sincerely: ⓓ Correct as is

♦ Write a persuasive letter to convince your local government that licenses
for baby-sitters are necessary or unnecessary. Be sure to include facts and
opinions to support your argument and persuade your audience.

10

Verbs

♦ Fill in the bubble next to the action verb in each sentence.

Action Verbs
1. I watched a video about kiwi birds.

　ⓐ watched　　　　　　ⓑ video

　ⓒ birds　　　　　　　ⓓ about

Action Verbs
2. Kiwis sleep during the day.

　ⓐ Kiwis　　　　　　　ⓑ during

　ⓒ sleep　　　　　　　ⓓ day

♦ Fill in the bubble next to the direct object in each sentence.

Direct Objects
3. Kiwis often eat earthworms.

　ⓐ often　　　　　　　ⓑ earthworms

　ⓒ eat　　　　　　　　ⓓ Kiwis

Direct Objects
4. Brown feathers cover their bodies.

　ⓐ feathers　　　　　　ⓑ their

　ⓒ cover　　　　　　　ⓓ bodies

♦ Fill in the bubble next to the verb tense in **bold.**

Verb Tenses
5. Tonight, the birds _____ for food. **future tense**

　ⓐ will be hunt　　　　ⓑ will hunt

　ⓒ hunting　　　　　　ⓓ hunted

GO ON ➤

Name_____ Date_____

6. Last week, I _____ a kiwi at the zoo. **past tense**

ⓐ photograph   ⓑ will photograph

ⓒ photographing   ⓓ photographed

◆ Fill in the bubble next to the verb that agrees with the subject.

Subject-Verb Agreement

7. Sharon _____ very quickly.

ⓐ learn   ⓑ learns

ⓒ learning   ⓓ have learned

Subject-Verb Agreement

8. Marco and Jeff _____ drawing cartoon figures.

ⓐ practice   ⓑ practices

ⓒ practicing   ⓓ is practicing

◆ Fill in the bubble next to the correct spelling of the verb.

Spelling Present- and Past-Tense Verbs

9. Our class _____ drawings and photos in a big art show.

ⓐ displaied   ⓑ displaed

ⓒ displayed   ⓓ displayyed

◆ Fill in the bubble next to the correct sentence.

Commas

10. ⓐ We invited students, teachers, and parents to the show.

ⓑ We invited students teachers, and parents to the show.

ⓒ We invited students teachers and parents to the show.

ⓓ We invited students, teachers, and parents, to the show.

◆ Write an invitation to an art show in your school library. Include directions for getting there. Circle each present-tense verb, and underline each future-tense verb.

Verbs

♦ Fill in the bubble next to the sentence part named in **bold.**

Main Verbs and Helping Verbs
1. My class is studying dinosaurs this week. **main verb**

   ⓐ class   ⓑ is

   🌑 studying   ⓓ dinosaurs

Main Verbs and Helping Verbs
2. Some dinosaurs could eat leaves from the tops of trees. **helping verb**

   🌑 could   ⓑ eat

   ⓒ leaves   ⓓ from

♦ Fill in the bubble next to the best verb to complete the sentence.

Using Helping Verbs
3. I _____ learned a lot about dinosaurs.

   ⓐ am   ⓑ has

   ⓒ is   🌑 have

Using Helping Verbs
4. My friend Lissa _____ writing a report about dinosaur fossils.

   🌑 is   ⓑ has

   ⓒ are   ⓓ had

♦ Fill in the bubble next to the linking verb from each sentence.

Linking Verbs
5. Some dinosaurs were meat eaters.

   ⓐ dinosaurs   🌑 were

   ⓒ meat   ⓓ eaters

GO ON ➤

Name_____ Date_____

6. Their claws and teeth looked very fierce.

   ⓐ teeth   🅑 looked

   ⓒ very   ⓓ fierce

♦ Fill in the bubble next to the correct form of the verb in parentheses.

Irregular Verbs

7. Joshua (write) a mystery story for his class assignment.

   🅐 wrote   ⓑ written

   ⓒ writed   ⓓ wroted

Irregular Verbs

8. In his story, the main characters (begin) to search for a lost treasure.

   ⓐ beginned   ⓑ begined

   🅒 began   ⓓ begun

More Irregular Verbs

9. Luckily, they had (take) a shovel with them.

   ⓐ taked   ⓑ tooked

   ⓒ took   🅓 taken

♦ Fill in the bubble next to the contraction formed from the underlined words.

Contractions with Not

10. They <u>could not</u> believe their eyes!

   ⓐ could'nt   🅑 couldn't

   ⓒ couldon't   ⓓ couldnt'

♦ Have you ever solved a mystery? Maybe you found a lost pair of glasses or predicted the end of a book. Write a paragraph about the mystery and how you solved it. Circle each helping verb you use.

Verbs/Build Skills

♦ Fill in the bubble next to the sentence part named in **bold**.

Action Verbs

1. My sister talks on the telephone every afternoon. **action verb**

   ⓐ talks   ⓑ on

   ⓒ telephone   ⓓ every

Direct Objects

2. Yesterday she called six people. **direct object**

   ⓐ Yesterday   ⓑ called

   ⓒ six   ⓓ people

♦ Fill in the bubble next to the correct form of the verb to complete the sentence.

Verb Tenses

3. Tomorrow I _____ to her conversation.

   ⓐ have listened   ⓑ listened

   ⓒ will listen   ⓓ listening

Subject-Verb Agreement

4. She and Beth _____ about their plans for a slumber party.

   ⓐ chat   ⓑ chats

   ⓒ is chatting   ⓓ was chatting

♦ Fill in the bubble next to the word best completes each sentence.

Prefixes and Suffixes

5. They were _____, and the line went dead.

   ⓐ preconnected   ⓑ disconnected

   ⓒ connectedment   ⓓ biconnected

GO ON ➤

Prefixes and Suffixes

6. When my sister invited me to the party, my face showed my _____.

    ⓐ imastonish   ⓑ astonishless

    ⓒ astonishment   ⓓ astonishist

♦ Fill in the bubble next to the best answer to each question.

Use an Encyclopedia

7. How are the articles in an encyclopedia arranged?

    ⓐ alphabetically by topic   ⓑ by date

    ⓒ alphabetically by author's name   ⓓ by importance

Use an Encyclopedia

8. What does a cross-reference in an encyclopedia article do?

    ⓐ It gives the title of the article.

    ⓑ It leads you to other articles on the topic.

    ⓒ It lists books in which you can read about the topic.

    ⓓ It tells the volume in which the article appears.

Use an Encyclopedia

9. Suppose you wanted to learn where butterflies lay their eggs. What keyword should you look under in an encyclopedia to find the most information?

    ⓐ where   ⓑ butterflies

    ⓒ lay   ⓓ eggs

Use an Encyclopedia

10. Suppose you wanted to learn about how glaciers are formed. What keyword should you type in to find information on this topic in an on-line encyclopedia?

    ⓐ ice   ⓑ formed

    ⓒ computer   ⓓ glaciers

♦ Write directions telling how to get from one place to another in your neighborhood. Underline each time-order word, and circle each spatial word that you use.

    10

Verbs/Explanatory Writing

♦ Fill in the bubble next to the correct answer.

Spelling Present- and Past-Tense Verbs

1. During much of the year, snowfall _____ the state of Alaska.

   ⓐ burys   ⬤ⓑ buries

   ⓒ bures   ⓓ buryes

Spelling Present- and Past-Tense Verbs

2. Mount McKinley _____ a height of more than 20,000 feet.

   ⓐ reachs   ⓑ reachses

   ⬤ⓒ reaches   ⓓ reacheses

Commas

3. ⬤ⓐ Yes, I visited Alaska.   ⓑ Yes I visited Alaska.

   ⓒ Yes, I visited, Alaska.   ⓓ Yes I, visited Alaska.

Commas

4. ⓐ Your photograph, of the bald eagle, is amazing Ricardo.

   ⓑ Your photograph, of the bald eagle is amazing, Ricardo.

   ⓒ Your photograph, of the bald eagle is amazing Ricardo.

   ⬤ⓓ Your photograph of the bald eagle is amazing, Ricardo.

♦ Fill in the bubble next to the sentence part named in **bold.**

Main Verbs and Helping Verbs

5. You should have climbed an Alaskan volcano. **main verb**

   ⓐ should   ⓑ have

   ⬤ⓒ climbed   ⓓ volcano

GO ON ▶

Main Verbs and Helping Verbs

6. I am trying to imagine twenty hours of sunlight a day.
helping verb

   ⓐ imagine   ⓑ **am**

   ⓒ I   ⓓ to

♦ Fill in the bubble next to the best answer.

Writing

7. What is the purpose of explanatory writing?

   ⓐ to tell how two subjects are alike

   ⓑ to tell a story about the author

   ⓒ to persuade the audience

   ⓓ **to give step-by-step directions**

Writing

8. Which of these would be the best topic for explanatory writing?

   ⓐ Insects and Gardens   ⓑ **How to Build a Kite**

   ⓒ A Visit to a Swamp   ⓓ More Vacation Days!

Writing

9. Which of these is a time-order word?

   ⓐ **finally**   ⓑ above

   ⓒ because   ⓓ however

Writing

10. Which of these is a spatial word?

    ⓐ since   ⓑ unlike

    ⓒ **beside**   ⓓ when

♦ Make a flowchart showing the steps you follow when you add
two fractions. Use your flowchart to help you write a paragraph
for a younger student explaining how to add fractions.

Verbs/Explanatory Writing

♦ Fill in the bubble next to the correct form of the verb in parentheses.

Linking Verbs

1. The deep sea (be) the largest habitat on earth.

   ⓐ is   ⓑ were

   ⓒ are   ⓓ am

Irregular Verbs

2. Scientists have (make) amazing discoveries there.

   ⓐ maked   ⓑ maken

   ⓒ made   ⓓ maded

More Irregular Verbs

3. Divers have (take) photos of some very strange creatures.

   ⓐ taked   ⓑ tooken

   ⓒ took   ⓓ taken

More Irregular Verbs

4. I (know) the water would be choppy.

   ⓐ knew   ⓑ knowed

   ⓒ known   ⓓ knewed

♦ Fill in the bubble next to the correct form of the contraction.

Contractions with Not

5. I <u>did not</u> know how deep the ocean is.

   ⓐ did'nt   ⓑ didn't

   ⓒ didnt'   ⓓ did't

Contractions with Not

6. I <u>cannot</u> believe there are mountains underwater.

   ⓐ cann't   ⓑ can't

   ⓒ can'nt   ⓓ ca'nt

GO ON ➡

Name_____ Date_____

♦ Fill in the bubble next to the best way to write each section.

I did an experiment to find out what would happen to a seed that was planted upside down. <u>I used a jar, soil, sunflower seeds and water.</u>
7

First, I filled the jar with soil and poked in the seeds. I planted some seeds with the pointed end up. <u>Others was</u> planted with the pointed end down.
8
<u>I carried</u> the jar to a sunny window and watered the seeds. Soon, I saw that the
9
<u>seeds has begun</u> to grow. Every stem pointed up. Plants grow no matter which
10
way you plant them.

Commas
7. ⓐ I used a jar, soil, sunflower seeds and, water.

ⓑ I used a jar, soil, sunflower seeds, and water.

ⓒ I used a jar, soil, sunflower, seeds, and water.

ⓓ Correct as is

Linking Verbs
8. ⓐ Others were ⓑ Others is

ⓒ Others being ⓓ Correct as is

Spelling Present- and Past-Tense Verbs
9. ⓐ I carred ⓑ I carryd

ⓒ I carryed ⓓ Correct as is

Using Helping Verbs
10. ⓐ seeds were begun ⓑ seeds was begun

ⓒ seeds had begun ⓓ Correct as is

♦ Think of a snack you know how to prepare, such as cheese and crackers or fruit salad. Write step-by-step instructions explaining how to prepare this snack.

Adjectives

♦ Fill in the bubble next to an adjective from the sentence.

Adjectives

1. My parents and I went on a short trip last weekend.
   - ⓐ parents
   - ⬤ⓑ **short**
   - ⓒ trip
   - ⓓ weekend

Adjectives

2. Fifty relatives attended the family reunion.
   - ⬤ⓐ **Fifty**
   - ⓑ relatives
   - ⓒ attended
   - ⓓ reunion

Adjectives

3. The stories about my great-grandparents were interesting.
   - ⓐ stories
   - ⓑ about
   - ⓒ were
   - ⬤ⓓ **interesting**

♦ Fill in the bubble next to the article that best completes each sentence.

Articles

4. I had two tacos and _____ piece of watermelon for lunch.
   - ⬤ⓐ **a**
   - ⓑ those
   - ⓒ an
   - ⓓ these

Articles

5. We enjoyed looking at _____ photograph albums.
   - ⓐ a
   - ⬤ⓑ **the**
   - ⓒ an
   - ⓓ that

GO ON ➤

Articles

6. The family reunion was _____ amazing success.

   ⓐ a   ⓑ the

   ⓒ an   ⓓ those

♦ Fill in the bubble next to the correct demonstrative adjective.

Demonstrative Adjectives

7. I found information about the elf owl in _____ book over there.

   ⓐ this   ⓑ that

   ⓒ these   ⓓ those

Demonstrative Adjectives

8. _____ photographs over here show how small elf owls are.

   ⓐ This   ⓑ That

   ⓒ These   ⓓ Those

♦ Fill in the bubble next to the proper adjective formed from the noun in **bold type.**

Proper Adjectives

9. The largest bird is the _____ ostrich. **Africa**

   ⓐ Africanese   ⓑ Africish

   ⓒ Africadian   ⓓ African

Proper Adjectives

10. The _____ vulture is also a large bird. **South America**

   ⓐ South American   ⓑ South America

   ⓒ South Americian   ⓓ Southian America

♦ Imagine that a nearby zoo has obtained some new animals. Write a paragraph advertising the animals' arrival. Use vivid adjectives so that people will want to visit the zoo. Circle each adjective.

Adjectives

♦ Fill in the bubble next to the form of the adjective that best completes the sentence.

Comparative and Superlative Adjectives

1. The Sahara is the _____ desert in the world.

   ⓐ largeer   ⓑ largeest

   ⓒ larger   ⬤ largest

Comparative and Superlative Adjectives

2. Nights in a desert are much _____ than days.

   ⓐ coldder   ⓑ coldst

   ⬤ colder   ⓓ coldest

Comparing with More and Most

3. The Brazilian rainforest is much _____ than a desert.

   ⓐ more wetter   ⓑ most wet

   ⬤ wetter   ⓓ wettest

Comparing with More and Most

4. Some people think that deserts are the _____ places on Earth.

   ⓐ more interesting   ⬤ most interesting

   ⓒ more interestinger   ⓓ most interestingest

Comparing with Good and Bad

5. I think a forest is a _____ place to visit than a desert.

   ⬤ better   ⓑ best

   ⓒ gooder   ⓓ goodest

Comparing with Good and Bad

6. The desert is the _____ place to go if you hate hot, dry weather.

   ⓐ worse   ⬤ worst

   ⓒ more worst   ⓓ most worst

GO ON ➡

♦ Fill in the bubble next to the best way to combine the sentences.

Adjectives

7. My family is moving into a house. The house is gray.

   ⓐ My family is moving into a gray house.

   ⓑ My family is moving into a house the house is gray.

   ⓒ My family is moving into a house gray.

   ⓓ My family is moving into a house, the house is gray.

Adjectives

8. We packed our belongings in boxes. The boxes were sturdy.

   ⓐ We packed our belongings in boxes, were sturdy.

   ⓑ We packed our belongings in sturdy boxes.

   ⓒ We packed our belongings in boxes, the boxes were sturdy.

   ⓓ We packed our belongings in boxes, sturdy.

♦ Fill in the bubble next to the correct abbreviation for the underlined word.

Abbreviations

9. <u>Doctor</u> Ross moved to our city on October 12.

   ⓐ Dr.   ⓑ Doc.

   ⓒ Dr   ⓓ Doc

Abbreviations

10. His office address is 205 Brower <u>Road</u>.

    ⓐ ro.   ⓑ Ro.

    ⓒ rd.   ⓓ Rd.

♦ Imagine that you are a teacher. Write a journal entry describing your day at work. Use at least three comparative or superlative adjectives in your entry. Underline the comparative adjectives once and the superlative adjectives twice.

Adjectives/Build Skills

♦ Fill in the bubble next to the part of the sentence named in **bold type.**

Adjectives

1. I read a terrific book about animals from Mexico. **adjective**

   ⓐ read   ⓑ book

   ● terrific   ⓓ animals

Articles

2. It says that my pet iguana may have come from a jungle in Mexico. **article**

   ⓐ and   ⓑ says

   ⓒ to   ● a

♦ Fill in the bubble next to the correct demonstrative adjective.

Demonstrative Adjectives

3. I found the book on one of _____ shelves over there.

   ⓐ this   ⓑ these

   ⓒ that   ● those

Demonstrative Adjectives

4. _____ book in my hand tells about lots of strange animals.

   ● This   ⓑ These

   ⓒ That   ⓓ Those

♦ Fill in the bubble next to the synonym of the underlined word.

Synonyms and Antonyms

5. Some <u>tiny</u> tree frogs are bright and colorful.

   ⓐ dull   ⓑ weak

   ● small   ⓓ large

GO ON ➤

♦ Fill in the bubble next to the antonym of the underlined word.

Synonyms and Antonyms

6. <u>Thick</u> vines coil around the trees and across the ground.

ⓐ thin   ⓑ dense

ⓒ tangled   ⓓ short

♦ Fill in the bubble next to the best answer.

Use Time Lines and Historical Maps

7. What is a time line?

ⓐ a table that includes places   **ⓑ** a diagram of a series of events

ⓒ a map of ancient nations   ⓓ a drawing of an artifact

Use Time Lines and Historical Maps

8. How are the events on a time line arranged?

ⓐ in alphabetical order   ⓑ in order of importance

ⓒ in the order they happened   ⓓ from west to east

Use Time Lines and Historical Maps

9. Which of these does a historical map show?

ⓐ events in the future   **ⓑ** where past events took place

ⓒ why past events took place   ⓓ what people once looked like

Use Time Lines and Historical Maps

10. Which question could best be answered with a historical map?

ⓐ Why was the Erie Canal built?

ⓑ What route did the explorers Lewis and Clark follow?

ⓒ When did Abraham Lincoln become president?

ⓓ Did George Washington wear a wig?

♦ Imagine that you are living 200 years ago. Write a letter to a friend explaining how you spent the summer. Use an outline to organize your ideas. Include detailed information in your letter.

◻ 10

Adjectives/Expository Writing

♦ Fill in the bubble next to the correct adjective form of the word in **bold.**

Proper Adjectives

1. My grandmother gave me a book of _____ fables. **Africa**

   ⓐ Africese   ⓑ African

   ⓒ Africa   ⓓ Africish

Proper Adjectives

2. Last year, she gave me a collection of _____ short stories. **Japan**

   ⓐ Japanish   ⓑ Japanian

   ⓒ Japanese   ⓓ Japan

Comparative and Superlative Adjectives

3. This book is _____ than the one I read last week. **funny**

   ⓐ funnyest   ⓑ funny

   ⓒ funniest   ⓓ funnier

Comparative and Superlative Adjectives

4. It has to be the _____ story ever written. **strange**

   ⓐ strangeest   ⓑ strange

   ⓒ strangest   ⓓ stranger

Comparing with More and Most

5. The main character is the _____ cat in the world. **unusual**

   ⓐ most unusual   ⓑ more unusual

   ⓒ most unusualest   ⓓ more unusualer

Comparing with More and Most

6. The cat was _____ to the king than his treasure. **valuable**

   ⓐ valuabler   ⓑ valuablest

   ⓒ more valuable   ⓓ most valuable   **GO ON** ▶

Name_____ Date_____

♦ Fill in the bubble next to the best answer.

Writing

7. What is the main purpose of expository writing?

   ⓐ to present the author's opinions on a topic

   🅑 to give facts and information about a topic

   ⓒ to tell how two topics are different

   ⓓ to tell about a personal experience

Writing

8. Which of these would be the best topic for expository writing?

   🅐 The Paintings of Claude Monet

   ⓑ How to Clean a Paintbrush

   ⓒ My Adventure at the Museum

   ⓓ Why Watercolors Are Better Than Oil Paints

Writing

9. Which of the following is *not* a transitional word?

   ⓐ before   ⓑ however

   ⓒ finally   🅓 interesting

Writing

10. What is the most important reason to use a variety of sources in expository writing?

   🅐 to obtain accurate and complete information

   ⓑ to practice using library reference books

   ⓒ to help you organize your ideas

   ⓓ to help you connect the events and ideas in your writing

♦ Write an article about your favorite playground for the magazine, *Playgrounds of America*. Use an outline to organize your ideas before you begin. Be sure to end your report by drawing a conclusion.

10

Adjectives/Expository Writing

♦ Fill in the bubble next to the correct form of the adjective.

Comparing with Good *and* Bad

1. The _____ places to view comets are far away from cities.

   ⓐ bestest
   ⓑ better
   ⓒ best
   ⓓ most best

Comparing with Good *and* Bad

2. For comet-viewing, foggy skies are _____ than clear skies.

   ⓐ worser
   ⓑ worse
   ⓒ more bad
   ⓓ badder

♦ Fill in the bubble next to the best way to combine the sentences.

Adjectives

3. A comet has a long tail. Its tail is icy.

   ⓐ A comet has a long, icy tail.
   ⓑ A comet has a long tail icy.
   ⓒ A comet has a long tail it is icy.
   ⓓ A comet has a long tail, icy tail.

Adjectives

4. Astronomers sighted a comet around 240 B.C. They were Chinese.

   ⓐ Chinese, astronomers sighted a comet around 240 B.C.
   ⓑ Astronomers sighted a comet around 240 B.C. Chinese.
   ⓒ Chinese astronomers sighted a comet around 240 B.C.
   ⓓ Astronomers Chinese sighted a comet around 240 B.C.

♦ Fill in the bubble next to the correct abbreviation for the underlined word.

Abbreviations

5. Each May and <u>October</u>, Earth passes through the comet's orbit.

   ⓐ Octob.
   ⓑ Oct.
   ⓒ Octob
   ⓓ Oct

GO ON ➡

Abbreviations

6. <u>Mister</u> Lewis told us that a comet struck Jupiter in 1994.

   ⓐ Mr.   ⓑ Mr

   ⓒ mr.   ⓓ mr

◆ Fill in the bubble next to the best way to write each section.

> Paul Revere was <u>the brave American patriot</u>. <u>He is famous for his ride. His</u>
>   **7**   **8**
> <u>ride was at midnight</u>. He warned the colonists in Massachusetts that British
> soldiers were on their way to arrest Samuel Adams and John Hancock. <u>This</u>
>   **9**
> <u>men</u> were leaders of a group that supported the American Revolution. Revere
> borrowed <u>the fastest horse in all of Boston</u> to alert the colonists.
>   **10**

Articles

7. ⓐ an brave American patriot   ⓑ a brave American patriot

   ⓒ brave American patriot   ⓓ Correct as is

Adjectives

8. ⓐ He is famous for his midnight   ⓑ He is famous for midnight
       ride.   his ride.

   ⓒ he is famous for his ride.   ⓓ Correct as is

Demonstrative Adjectives

9. ⓐ That men   ⓑ Them men

   ⓒ These men   ⓓ Correct as is

Comparing with More and Most

10. ⓐ the more fast horse in all   ⓑ the most fast horse in all
       of Boston   of Boston

   ⓒ the faster horse in all of Boston   ⓓ Correct as is

◆ Imagine that you have a pen pal who lives in China. Write a letter to
   your pen pal, telling about your school and include facts and details.

Pronouns

♦ Fill in the bubble next to the pronoun from the sentence.

Pronouns
1. Ms. Bowen asked us to write a story about yesterday's field trip.
   ⓐ us   ⓑ to
   ⓒ a   ⓓ about

Pronouns
2. We went to the planetarium with the other fifth-grade classes.
   ⓐ We   ⓑ the
   ⓒ with   ⓓ other

Pronouns
3. Karen and I sat together in the front row.
   ⓐ and   ⓑ I
   ⓒ together   ⓓ in

♦ Fill in the bubble next to the correct pronoun to replace the underlined words.

Subject Pronouns
4. The planetarium was amazing.
   ⓐ He   ⓑ They
   ⓒ It   ⓓ Them

Subject Pronouns
5. The tour guides taught us about telescopes and constellations.
   ⓐ We   ⓑ They
   ⓒ It   ⓓ Them

GO ON ➡

Subject Pronouns

6. <u>Robert</u> wants to visit the planetarium again.

ⓐ Me   ⓑ They

ⓒ I   ⓓ He

♦ Fill in the bubble next to the pronoun that correctly completes the sentence.

Object Pronoun

7. My father brought home a bike for _____.

ⓐ me   ⓑ we

ⓒ she   ⓓ I

Object Pronoun

8. My brother Hisham rode _____ all around the neighborhood.

ⓐ we   ⓑ they

ⓒ he   ⓓ it

♦ Fill in the bubble next to the correct way to use a colon or a hyphen.

Colons and Hyphens

9. My _____ said he rode like an expert.

ⓐ half:sister Tina   ⓑ half sister-Tina

ⓒ half sister:Tina   ⓓ half-sister Tina

Colons and Hyphens

10. Hisham woke up at _____ this morning to ride the bike again.

ⓐ 5-30   ⓑ 530:

ⓒ 5:30   ⓓ 5-30:

♦ Write a paragraph comparing two activities that you enjoy. Tell how these activities are alike and how they are different. Circle the subject pronouns in your paragraph, and draw boxes around the object pronouns.

Pronouns

♦ Fill in the bubble next to the verb that correctly completes the sentence.

Pronoun-Verb Agreement

1. She _____ her horse Banner in horse shows.
   - ⓐ ride
   - ⓑ rides
   - ⓒ have ridden
   - ⓓ are riding

Pronoun-Verb Agreement

2. I _____ Elizabeth from the stands.
   - ⓐ were watching
   - ⓑ has watched
   - ⓒ watch
   - ⓓ watches

Pronoun-Verb Agreement

3. Each weekend, we _____ to a new show.
   - ⓐ travels
   - ⓑ am traveling
   - ⓒ does travel
   - ⓓ travel

♦ Fill in the bubble next to the best way to combine the sentences.

Combining Sentences: Subject and Object Pronouns

4. She grooms and saddles the horse. I groom and saddle the horse.
   - ⓐ She, and I, grooms and saddles the horse.
   - ⓑ She and I grooms and saddles the horse.
   - ⓒ She and I groom and saddle the horse.
   - ⓓ She grooms and saddles the horse I groom and saddle the horse.

Combining Sentences: Subject and Object Pronouns

5. Elizabeth tries to amaze them. Elizabeth tries to amaze me.
   - ⓐ Elizabeth tries to amaze them and me.
   - ⓑ Elizabeth tries to amaze them and amaze me.
   - ⓒ Elizabeth tries to amaze them, and me.
   - ⓓ Elizabeth tries to amaze them Elizabeth tries to amaze me.

GO ON ➤

Name_____ Date_____

Combining Sentences: Subject and Object Pronouns

6. She cleans out the stall. He cleans out the stall.

    ⓐ She cleans out the stall and he cleans.

    ⓑ She cleans out the stall and he.

    ⓒ She and he cleans out the stall.

    ⓓ They clean out the stall.

♦ Fill in the bubble next to the pronoun that correctly completes the sentence.

Possessive Pronouns

7. _____ brother and I went on a canoe trip in Colorado.

    ⓐ My   ⓑ Yours

    ⓒ Hers   ⓓ Mine

Possessive Pronouns

8. That green canoe in the garage is _____.

    ⓐ they   ⓑ their

    ⓒ ours   ⓓ our

♦ Fill in the bubble next to the contraction formed from the underlined words.

Contractions: Pronouns and Verbs

9. <u>We are</u> going canoeing in New York next year.

    ⓐ Were   **ⓑ** We're

    ⓒ We'are   ⓓ Wer'e

Contractions: Pronouns and Verbs

10. <u>It is</u> exciting to paddle down a river.

    ⓐ It's   ⓑ Its'

    ⓒ Its   ⓓ I'ts

♦ Choose two seasons of the year and write a composition comparing them for your teacher. End your comparison with a strong conclusion. Underline each possessive pronoun you use.

Pronouns/Build Skills

♦ Fill in the bubble next to a pronoun from the sentence.

Pronouns

1. They traveled to America on a ship named the *Mayflower*.

ⓐ They   ⓑ to

ⓒ a   ⓓ the

Pronouns

2. On September 16, 1620, it left England and headed across the ocean.

ⓐ On   ⓑ it

ⓒ and   ⓓ across

♦ Fill in the bubble next to the correct pronoun to replace the underlined words.

Subject Pronouns

3. My grandfather wrote a book about the voyage of the *Mayflower*.

ⓐ He   ⓑ You

ⓒ Him   ⓓ Your

Subject Pronouns

4. My mother and I read his book last year.

ⓐ Us   ⓑ They

ⓒ We   ⓓ She

♦ Fill in the bubble next to the vivid word that best replaces the underlined word.

Word Choice

5. Icy storm waves <u>hit</u> the deck of the ship.

ⓐ reached   ⓑ pounded

ⓒ missed   ⓓ touched

GO ON ▶

Word Choice

6. The Pilgrims were <u>tired</u> when the *Mayflower* arrived at America.

   ⓐ sad

   ⓒ exhausted

   ⓑ quiet

   ⓓ hungry

♦ Fill in the bubble next to the correct answer to the question.

Use a Dictionary

7. How are the words in a dictionary arranged?

   ⓐ in alphabetical order

   ⓒ in order of importance

   ⓑ by parts of speech

   ⓓ by number of meanings

Use a Dictionary

8. What do the guide words in a dictionary tell you?

   ⓐ how to pronounce a word

   ⓒ the definition of a word

   ⓑ the first and last entry words on a page

   ⓓ the parts of speech a word can be

Use a Dictionary

9. What does an example sentence in a dictionary show you?

   ⓐ how to pronounce a word

   ⓒ how a word is used in a sentence

   ⓑ how to form the plural of a word

   ⓓ how many meanings a word has

Use a Dictionary

10. Which part of a dictionary tells you how to say the vowels and consonants?

   ⓐ parts of speech

   ⓒ guide words

   ⓑ definitions

   ⓓ pronunciation key

♦ What types of transportation have you used? Choose two types, such as a bike and a train. Write a journal entry comparing the two. Use sensory details and vivid language to describe how they are alike and how they are different.

10

Pronouns/Writing That Compares

♦ Fill in the bubble next to the correct pronoun to replace the underlined words.

Object Pronouns

1. My parents are planning a trip for <u>themselves, my sister, and me</u>.

   (a) ours   (b) our

   (c) we   ● (d) us

Object Pronouns

2. They check the car and fill <u>the car</u> with gas.

   (a) him   ● (b) it

   (c) them   (d) its

♦ Fill in the bubble next to the word or phrase that correctly completes the sentence.

Colons and Hyphens

3. We count _____ chipmunks near the parking lot.

   ● (a) twenty-seven   (b) twentyseven

   (c) twenty:seven   (d) twenty seven

Colons and Hyphens

4. We got the campfire started by _____.

   (a) 7 30-P.M.   (b) 7 30:P.M.

   ● (c) 7:30 P.M.   (d) 7-30 P.M.

♦ Fill in the bubble next to the verb that correctly completes the sentence.

Pronoun-Verb Agreement

5. We _____ up the tent while my sister cooks dinner.

   ● (a) set   (b) sets

   (c) setting   (d) is setting

GO ON ➡

Pronoun-Verb Agreement

6. She _____ her sleeping bag under a large tree.

    ⓐ unroll   **ⓑ unrolls**

    ⓒ unrolling   ⓓ am unrolling

♦ Fill in the bubble next to the correct answer to the question.

Writing

7. What is the purpose of writing that compares?

    ⓐ to persuade readers to agree with an opinion

    ⓑ to tell how two topics are like and unlike each other

    ⓒ to tell about events that happened to the writer

    ⓓ to give readers step-by-step instructions

Writing

8. Which of these is a contrast word, used to show a difference?

    ⓐ both   ⓑ later

    ⓒ however   ⓓ first

Writing

9. Which of these is a comparison word or phrase, used to show a similarity?

    ⓐ salty   ⓑ next

    ⓒ in the case of   **ⓓ like**

Writing

10. Which of these would be the best topic for writing that compares?

    ⓐ Grasshoppers and Crickets   ⓑ Making Tacos

    ⓒ The Egyptian Pyramids   ⓓ My Best Friend

♦ Choose two school subjects, such as art and social studies. Make a compare-and-contrast chart that shows how the subjects are alike and how they are different. Use your chart to write a paragraph that compares the two subjects.

Pronouns/Writing That Compares

♦ Fill in the bubble next to the best way to combine the sentences.

Combining Sentences: Subject and Object Pronouns

1. She works on the project. I work on the project.

   ⓐ She and I work on the project.   ⓑ She and me work on the project.

   ⓒ She works on the project and I.   ⓓ She and I works on the project.

Combining Sentences: Subject and Object Pronouns

2. Maria practices in front of me. Maria practices in front of him.

   ⓐ Maria practices in front of me, him.

   ⓑ Maria practices in front of me in front of him.

   ⓒ Maria practice in front of me.

   ⓓ Maria practices in front of him and me.

♦ Fill in the bubble next to the pronoun that correctly completes the sentence.

Possessive Pronouns

3. Maria and I won first prize for _____ project.

   ⓐ we   ⓑ our

   ⓒ ours   ⓓ us

Possessive Pronouns

4. Ryan and Lin did _____ on black holes.

   ⓐ their   ⓑ their's

   ⓒ theirs   ⓓ theirs'

♦ Fill in the bubble next to the contraction formed from the underlined words.

Contractions: Pronoun and Verb

5. <u>They are</u> going to enter the science fair again next year.

   ⓐ They're   ⓑ The're

   ⓒ They'are   ⓓ Theyre

GO ON ▶

Contractions: Pronoun and Verb

6. <u>You are</u> going to be amazed by our next project.

   ⓐ Your   **ⓑ** You're

   ⓒ Your'e   ⓓ Your'

♦ Read the passage. Fill in the bubble next to the best way to correct each underlined section. If the section needs no change, mark the choice *Correct as is*.

At first, <u>mine twin sisters</u> Jan and Jenni seem alike. <u>They has</u> the same
              7   **8**

wavy black hair. They sound similar when they talk, and both play soccer.

However, Jan and Jenni are also different. Jan wears dresses, and her

favorite hobby is playing the piano. Jenni, on the other hand, prefers <u>jeans</u>
                                                          9

<u>and T-shirts</u> instead of fancy clothes. Her favorite hobby is reading. My

sisters' similarities and differences <u>make they</u> special to me.
                                            10

Possessive Pronouns

7. ⓐ my' twin sisters   ⓑ my twin sisters'

    ⓒ my twin sisters   ⓓ Correct as is

Pronoun-Verb Agreement

8. ⓐ Them have   ⓑ Them has

    ⓒ They have   ⓓ Correct as is

Colons and Hyphens

9. ⓐ jeans and Tshirts   ⓑ jeans and T:shirts

    ⓒ jeans-and-Tshirts   **ⓓ** Correct as is

Object Pronouns

10. ⓐ make their   **ⓑ** make them

    ⓒ make thems   ⓓ Correct as is

♦ Choose two ways to exercise, and write a composition for your teacher comparing them. Use vivid and precise words to make your meaning clear.

Adverbs, Prepositions, and Interjections

♦ Fill in the bubble next to the adverb from the sentence.

Adverbs

1. We always decorate the room with purple and gold streamers.

ⓐ gold   ⓑ room

ⓒ decorate   ⓓ **always**

Adverbs

2. I carefully set the flowers on the table.

ⓐ **carefully**   ⓑ set

ⓒ flowers   ⓓ table

Adverbs Before Adjectives and Adverbs

3. We are almost ready for the spring awards dinner.

ⓐ are   ⓑ **almost**

ⓒ dinner   ⓓ for

Adverbs Before Adjectives and Adverbs

4. This year's event is very exciting.

ⓐ This   ⓑ event

ⓒ **very**   ⓓ exciting

♦ Fill in the bubble next to the form of the adverb that best completes the sentence.

Comparing with Adverbs

5. The preparations for the dinner go _____ at the beginning.

ⓐ more slow   ⓑ **more slowly**

ⓒ slowlier   ⓓ slowliest

Comparing with Adverbs

6. Of all my siblings, my brother cooks _____.

ⓐ oftener   ⓑ oftenest

ⓒ more oftener   ⓓ **most often**

GO ON ▶

♦ Fill in the bubble next to the word or words that best complete the sentence.

Negatives

7. Doesn't _____ want to watch the soccer game?

    ⓐ no one   **ⓑ anyone**

    ⓒ nobody   ⓓ ever

Negatives

8. Roberto has _____ missed a goal before.

    ⓐ never   ⓑ not never

    ⓒ no   ⓓ ever

♦ Fill in the bubble next to the correct sentence.

Punctuation in Dialogue

9. ⓐ "I can't believe I missed it! said Roberto."

    ⓑ "I can't believe I missed it! said" Roberto.

    ⓒ "I can't believe I missed it!", said Roberto.

    ⓓ "I can't believe I missed it!" said Roberto.

Punctuation in Dialogue

10. ⓐ "Tim replied You're still our star kicker, Roberto."

    ⓑ Tim replied "you're still our star kicker, Roberto."

    ⓒ Tim replied, "You're still our star kicker, Roberto."

    ⓓ "Tim replied, you're still our star kicker, Roberto."

♦ Write a short story about a soccer team that never wins a game. Include dialogue in your story to make your characters seem believable. Draw a circle around each adverb you use.

Adverbs, Prepositions, and Interjections

♦ Fill in the bubble next to the preposition from the sentence.

Prepositions
1. Beth and I climbed up the steep path.

    ⓐ I   **ⓑ up**

    ⓒ the   ⓓ path

Prepositions
2. At the top, we rested and snacked.

    ⓐ At   ⓑ top

    ⓒ we   ⓓ and

♦ Fill in the bubble next to the prepositional phrase from the sentence.

Prepositional Phrases
3. Across the stream, we saw a raccoon.

    ⓐ we saw   ⓑ the stream

    ⓒ saw a raccoon   **ⓓ Across the stream**

Prepositional Phrases
4. Beth spied two squirrels in a tall tree.

    ⓐ spied two squirrels   ⓑ Beth spied

    ⓒ in a tall tree   ⓓ a tall tree

♦ Fill in the bubble next to the best pronoun to replace the underlined words.

Object Pronouns in Prepositional Phrases
5. I took a photograph of <u>the squirrels</u>.

    ⓐ they   **ⓑ them**

    ⓒ their   ⓓ theirs

Object Pronouns in Prepositional Phrases
6. It was a fun day of hiking for <u>Beth and me</u>.

    ⓐ she   ⓑ we

    ⓒ her   **ⓓ us**

GO ON ➤

Name_____ Date_____

♦ Fill in the bubble next to the interjection in the sentence.

Interjections

7. Well, my friend and I saw a film about space travel.

    ⓐ Well   ⓑ about

    ⓒ space travel   ⓓ my friend

Interjections

8. Wow! The first landing on the moon was amazing!

    ⓐ first   ⓑ landing

    ⓒ Wow   ⓓ amazing

♦ Fill in the bubble next to the best way to combine the sentences using the conjunction in **bold type.**

Complex Sentences

9. The film is worth seeing again. It is long. **although**

    ⓐ The film although worth seeing again it is long.

    ⓑ Although it is long, the film is worth seeing again.

    ⓒ The film is worth seeing again, and although it is long.

    ⓓ It is long although, the film is worth seeing again.

♦ Fill in the bubble next to the correct sentence.

Commas with Introductory Prepositional Phrases and Interjections

10. ⓐ After the film, my friend and I were glad we had gone.

    ⓑ After, the film my friend and I were glad we had gone.

    ⓒ After the film. My friend and I were glad we had gone.

    ⓓ After the film my friend and I, were glad we had gone.

♦ Write a paragraph about a show or a movie that you have seen. Use at least three complex sentences in your paragraph. Draw a box around the conjunctions in the complex sentences.

Adverbs, Prepositions, and Interjections/ Build Skills

♦ Fill in the bubble next to the adverb from the sentence.

Adverbs

1. The bulbs in my garden have grown rapidly.
   - ⓐ bulbs
   - ⓒ grown
   - ⓑ have
   - ⬤ⓓ rapidly

Adverbs Before Adjectives and Adverbs

2. The tulips bloom for only two weeks.
   - ⓐ bloom
   - ⬤ⓒ only
   - ⓑ for
   - ⓓ two

♦ Fill in the bubble next to the form of the adverb that best completes the sentence.

Comparing with Adverbs

3. The sunflowers sprouted _____ of all.
   - ⓐ quicklier
   - ⓒ quickliest
   - ⓑ more quickly
   - ⬤ⓓ most quickly

Comparing with Adverbs

4. Last year, I had to weed my garden _____ than I do this year.
   - ⓐ most oftenest
   - ⓒ more oftener
   - ⬤ⓑ more often
   - ⓓ most often

♦ Fill in the bubble next to the figurative language in the sentence.

Figurative Language

5. Ripe raspberries gleam like rubies in the sunshine.
   - ⓐ raspberries
   - ⬤ⓒ like rubies
   - ⓑ sunshine
   - ⓓ Ripe

GO ON ➡

Name_____ Date_____

6. A flock of noisy crows laughed at me.

    ⓐ flock   ⓑ laughed

    ⓒ noisy crows   ⓓ at me

♦ Fill in the bubble next to the best answer to each question.

7. When using a card catalog, which type of card helps you find a book by Cynthia Rylant?

    ⓐ author card   ⓑ title card

    ⓒ subject card   ⓓ number card

8. What does the call number tell you?

    ⓐ where to find the book   ⓑ the year the book was printed

    ⓒ how many pages the book has   ⓓ how to contact the author

♦ Fill in the bubble next to the type of card that would help you answer the question.

9. Who wrote *The Birchbark House*?

    ⓐ author card   **ⓑ title card**

    ⓒ subject card   ⓓ number card

10. Does the library have a nonfiction book about horses?

    ⓐ author card   ⓑ title card

    ⓒ subject card   ⓓ number card

♦ Write a dialogue in which two friends are planning a surprise party. Be sure to use correct punctuation. Begin a new paragraph each time the speaker changes.

Adverbs, Prepositions, and Interjections/ Story Writing

♦ Fill in the bubble next to the best word or words to complete the sentence.

Negatives
1. Our field trip yesterday _____ start off well.

   ⓐ didn't never   ⓑ did not

   ⓒ never didn't   ⓓ not nohow

Negatives
2. _____ was ready to get on the bus when it arrived at school.

   ⬤ No one   ⓑ Not no one

   ⓒ Not nobody   ⓓ Never no body

♦ Fill in the bubble next to the type of word given in **bold type.**

Prepositions
3. None of the museum's doors were unlocked. **preposition**

   ⓐ None   ⬤ of

   ⓒ the   ⓓ were

Object of a Preposition
4. My class waited outside on the grass. **object of a preposition**

   ⓐ class   ⓑ My

   ⓒ on   ⬤ grass

Object of a Preposition
5. We were finally allowed into the building. **object of a preposition**

   ⓐ finally   ⓑ allowed

   ⓒ We   ⬤ building

GO ON ➡

Name_____ Date_____

♦ Fill in the bubble next to the best pronoun to replace the underlined words.

Object Pronouns in Prepositional Phrases

6. The tour guide apologized to <u>our teacher, Ms. Jacobs</u>.

   (a) she   (b) her
   (c) we   (d) us

♦ Fill in the bubble next to the best answer to the question.

Writing

7. Which of these is most often a feature of good story writing?

   (a) step-by-step instructions   (b) convincing reasons
   (c) a problem that is solved   (d) a conclusion based on facts

Writing

8. What does a story's setting describe?

   (a) when and where events take place   (b) how the story ends
   (c) the thoughts of the characters   (d) the actions of the characters

Writing

9. What is plot?

   (a) the dialogue in a story   (b) the title of a story
   (c) the main character of a story   (d) the sequence of events in a story

Writing

10. How does the writer of a story move the action along?

   (a) by using a satisfying ending
   (b) by describing the setting
   (c) by telling the characters' thoughts, words, and deeds
   (d) by using cause-and-effect words

♦ Think of a plot for a story about a class trip. Make a story map for the plot, and list characters and setting. Then use your map to write a story.

Story Writing

♦ Fill in the bubble next to the correct way to combine the sentences by using the conjunction in **bold type**.

Complex Sentences

1. The population of California grew rapidly. Gold was discovered. **after**

   ⓐ The population of California grew rapidly after gold was discovered.

   ⓑ The population of California grew rapidly and gold was discovered after.

   ⓒ The population of California grew rapidly after, gold was discovered.

   ⓓ The population of California grew rapidly gold was discovered after.

Complex Sentences

2. People came to California. They wanted to find gold. **because**

   ⓐ People came to California because, they wanted to find gold.

   ⓑ Because people came to California they wanted to find gold.

   ⓒ People came to California they wanted to find gold because.

   ⓓ People came to California because they wanted to find gold.

♦ Fill in the bubble next to the correct sentence.

Punctuation in Dialogue

3. ⓐ Phan asked, "Would you like to look for some gold?"

   ⓑ Phan asked "would you like to look for some gold?"

   ⓒ "Phan asked, would you like to look for some gold?"

   ⓓ Phan asked "Would you like to look for some gold"?

Interjections

4. ⓐ Well: where should we look?   ⓑ Well. where should we look?

   ⓒ Well! where should we look?   ⓓ Well, where should we look?

Commas with Introductory Prepositional Phrases and Interjections

5. ⓐ In the morning we can find some.   ⓑ In the morning, we can find some.

   ⓒ In the morning we can find, some   ⓓ In the morning, we can, find some.

GO ON ➤

Name_____ Date_____

6. ⓐ After the spring, thaw our luck will improve.

ⓑ After the spring thaw, our luck, will improve.

ⓒ After the spring thaw, our luck will improve.

ⓓ After the spring thaw our luck, will improve.

♦ Read the passage. Fill in the bubble next to the best way to correct each underlined section. If the section needs no change, mark the choice *Correct as is*.

Leah and her brother Sam heard a squeak from some bushes near the

path."<u>Yikes what is that</u>?" Leah whispered.
        7

Sam <u>didn't hear it no more</u>. "<u>Maybe it's a mouse</u>," he said.
        8   **9**

They searched the bushes and found a kitten. When it saw them, it squeaked

<u>loudlier than before</u>. "How about that?" asked Leah. "It thinks it's a mouse!"
   10

Interjections

7. ⓐ "Yikes: what is that?" ⓑ "Yikes! What is that?"

ⓒ "Yikes, What is that?" ⓓ Correct as is

Negatives

8. ⓐ didn't hear it none more ⓑ didn't hear it not more

ⓒ didn't hear it any more ⓓ Correct as is

Punctuation in Dialogue

9. ⓐ "Maybe it's a mouse, he said." ⓑ "Maybe it's a mouse." He said.

ⓒ "Maybe it's a mouse" he said. ⓓ Correct as is

Comparing with Adverbs

10. ⓐ more loudlier than before ⓑ more loudly than before

ⓒ loudly than before ⓓ Correct as is

♦ Imagine that two friends find a map showing where something is buried. Write a story about the friends and their experiences.